WITHDRAWN

325

LIFE, MIND, AND SPIRIT

LIFE, MIND, AND SPIRIT

BEING THE SECOND COURSE OF

THE GIFFORD LECTURES

DELIVERED IN THE UNIVERSITY OF ST ANDREWS IN
THE YEAR 1923 UNDER THE GENERAL TITLE OF

EMERGENT EVOLUTION

BY

C. LLOYD MORGAN, D.Sc., LL.D., F.R.S.

PROFESSOR EMERITUS IN THE UNIVERSITY OF BRISTOL

78297

NEW YORK
HENRY HOLT AND COMPANY
1926

DENISON UNIVERSITY
LIBRARY
GRANVILLE OHIO

Printed in Great Britain

DENISON UNIVERSITY
LIBRARY
GRANVILLE OHIO

3.38
3c

TO

E. C. M.

PREFACE

WHATEVER may have been the accepted meaning or meanings of the word " Evolution " prior to the middle of last century, Herbert Spencer in the course of the next decade or so set folk thinking afresh around the word and the concept he sought to embody in it—that of progress. Apart from questionable manner of statement in general form, apart from positive evidence in detail too obviously selected, here, at the heart of the matter, was a concept firmly contrasted and not confused with that of " dissolution," that, as he claimed, was applicable to all progress in cosmogony in the transmutation of species according to " the development hypothesis " in the conduct of men in social communities.

It met, and still meets, with strenuous and often bitter opposition. And why ? Not so much in regard to what it asserted, as in regard to what it denied—in the phrase, for example, " not by *manufacture* but by *evolution*." For the great majority of interested persons the head and front of Spencer's offending was in this negation, though there was sting also in the positive assertion that " creation by manufacture is a much lower thing than creation by evolution " (1858). Is it surprising that there were many who said, that there are some who still say :

The effect of this on religion must be disastrous. But what does the Rev. J. M. Wilson, Canon of Worcester, speaking for religion, now say ?   He says : " The discovery that the method of creation has been that of evolution should be regarded as a revelation to man of the Being and the working of God " (*Evolution in the Light of Modern Knowledge*, Aug. 1925, p. 512).

This may not have been Herbert Spencer's belief. Into that question I do not enter.   It is substantially my belief as expressed in the concluding lecture. To express it as best I can falls within Lord Gifford's injunction to the lecturers under his trust.

" Evolution not manufacture."   That surely can mean naught else than " natural not supernatural." In a sense that is so.   But is there not a sense in which the antithesis is becoming for many religious persons out of date ?   The sense in which it is so implies radically disparate dualism.   Hence it may be said : This or that for which a natural origin can be assigned is not supernatural ; but whatsoever must be attributed to supernatural origination is not natural.   Hence there can be nothing but questionable analogy to link modes of becoming in realms so diverse.   In man himself there is the life of the body to which a natural origin may perhaps be assigned.   But there is also the indwelling spirit that has entered into the possession of the body. This belongs to the quite other realm of spiritual beings.   Of free origination in this realm one can only say that it is not natural but supernatural.

What else, then, can one say ?   Without committing him to more than is here set down, one may

say with Dean Inge : " It may be a long time yet
before it is realised that any philosophical or religious
theory which separates man from nature—which
draws an impassable line anywhere across the field
of experience, whether the line be drawn at self-
consciousness or consciousness or anywhere else—is
untenable " (*Personal Idealism and Mysticism*, p. 146,
cf. p. 82). One may say with Canon Wilson : " It
has been the universal assumption in the past that
there were two separate spheres of existence, and
that these were wholly distinct in kind. They were
regarded respectively as natural and ' supernatural.'
Exceptional occurrences in the natural were to be
explained as caused by an irruption of the supernatural into the natural. . . . But now the human
mind . . . is rejecting the whole conception of this
irruption of one sphere into the other. It identifies
in kind what we have called the supernatural with
the natural. It makes the spiritual and the natural
continuous, and equally divine . . . not by denying
or degrading the supernatural, but by raising the
natural into entire continuity with it " (*Op. cit.*,
pp. 502–3).

Let me, however, lest I should implicate others
in a form of belief to which they do not fully sub-
scribe, state my own conclusion in my own way.
I put it thus : There is no disjunctive antithesis of
evolutionary progress and Divine purpose. The
question : Is there one *or* the other ? has no meaning
if there always be one *with* the other.

My chief concern is to present the point of view
of one who accepts both. How stands the matter,
then, in the light of emergent evolution ?

There is, I submit, an intelligible sense in which it may be said that, in the ascending hierarchy of stages of progress, regarded as manifestations of Divine Purpose, each higher stage is in turn *super*natural to that which precedes it.   In this sense life is supernatural to the inorganic ; reflective comprehension in thought is supernatural to naïve unreflective perception ; the religious attitude, with acknowledgment of Divine Purpose, is supernatural to the ethical attitude in social affairs.   For those who reach this highest stage, as they deem it, the religious attitude affords the supreme exemplar of the supernatural. It is distinctive of the spiritual man.   The ethical value of what the right-minded social person speaks of as " playing the game " is not lost ; the spiritual value of doing so in accordance with Divine Purpose, or " in God's sight," is gained.   It is this that is distinctive of the religious attitude as emergent in some persons.

But each supernatural in this sense, when it comes in due course, is a new and emergently higher character or quality of the natural—a further manifestation of the substantial unity of Divine Purpose. Within that unity all that is natural in evolutionary process of becoming is viewed in the supernatural attitude of a spiritual person as one with and not other than the " Working of God."   The stress for us is on a new *attitude*, for it is this that is, as I think, emergent.   Hence we may speak of a new " vision," and a new " heart," capable of a higher and richer form of joy.

The concept of Divine Purpose as timeless and omnipresent in substantial unity, but none the less manifested, and diversely manifested, at every here and now, is regarded by many religious persons as savouring too much of mysticism to meet the requirements of daily affairs. But, on the other hand, there are also religious persons who regard the alternative concept of a disparate realm of discarnate spirits as savouring too much of the mythical to meet the requirements of what, for them, is the deeper import of a spiritual attitude.

Now the realm of discarnate spirits is, for those who accept it, a distinctively supernatural realm. May one distinguish *this* concept of the supernatural as that which has its roots in primitive mythology ? In suggesting this one discloses one's personal bias. But why not, if it be the bias of honest conviction. My concept of the spiritual is avowedly monistic to the core. Mythology is avowedly pluralistic in a disparate realm of being.

There is no denying its widespread acceptance in a more or less modified form. For us, then, such questions arise as (1) How should we interpret its natural origin ? (2) What relation has it to what we have been led to regard as a spiritual attitude ? These come down to historical questions. Pending the verdict of history, it is at least open to us to surmise, as a matter of opinion based on some inquiry, that mythology had its origin in the exuberant creative imagination of primitive man ; and that its later refinement is traceable to the no less creative artistry of the poet in the old-time sense of " maker," that is, in Ben Jonson's words, of one who " feigneth and maketh a fable and writes things like the truth."

If this should be so, mythology is a creative product of the human mind, the outcome of feigning and fable—fable so real to the imagination as to be mistaken for acknowledged reality, even when criticism has entered on its task. Has it come down through the ages because primitive folk and some of their successors have deemed it so " like the truth " as hardly to be distinguishable therefrom ? Have the great poets taught us to substitute for " like the truth " *symbolic* " of the truth ? " Must we still take literally the pluralism of spiritist mythology ? May we not pass beyond all mythology and, even if it savour of mysticism, acknowledge the substantial unity of Divine Purpose in a realm of reality, one and indivisible ? These and the like are large questions here necessarily condensed in brief. I revert to a " may be." It may be that, in religious regard, mythology—and all that is supernatural in *that* sense —is the chaff to be winnowed from the pure grain of the teaching of Christianity.

Even so it may be that primitive mythology and its later refinements have had their due place in the progressive development of a monistic spiritual attitude. It is surely permissible, with the Biblical record before us, to regard the acceptance of supernatural mythology as a passing stage in the orderly unfolding of Divine Purpose. It may be that what for primitive and some later folk was a complex and elaborate drama, enacted on a stage that they peopled with fabulous spirits and alien gods, had first to be made and then unmade in order that a purified vision of one God might be reached through deeper spiritual insight.

And here emergent evolution has a suggestion to offer. If, as I shall have occasion to urge (p. 289), some measure of dissolution *at a lower level of emergence* be contributory to evolution *at a higher level*, it may well be that dissolution of the earlier mythological interpretation of current events has been contributory to the progressive evolution of that spiritual attitude towards Divine Purpose which, as I think, is emergent in religious persons throughout the ages of recorded human history.

Be this as it may, if we seek to face the facts of our world, we have to reckon with dissolution no less than with evolution—with regress no less than with progress. This opens up a difficult problem. I do not attempt to grapple with it. We must accept what we find. I find evolution ; and I find dissolution also. But may I not *select evolution as my theme* and deal only with lower-level dissolution in so far as it is contributory to higher-level evolution ? And may I not try to show in what way all evolutionary progress may be regarded as a manifestation and revelation (one must use some such words) of Divine Purpose ?

In order of exposition I treat first of emergent evolution and allied concepts before passing on to express the grounds of my belief in Divine Purpose. I do so because, as I think, the former, when it shall be more adequately handled than lies within my competence, may hold good whether the acknowledgment which the latter demands be accepted or not. The emphasis falls throughout on the evidence for a threshold of emergence—of life, of successive levels of mind, of spiritual attitude of mind. It does not lie within my province to pass into regions beyond the spiritual threshold. Important issues in Christian belief cannot be so much as mentioned. But with regard to the fundamental issue, centering in Divine Purpose, the purport of this Preface is to indicate in advance the conclusion which will be reached in the closing lecture. No doubt the discerning reader will see that the belief therein expressed colours much that I say on emergent evolution as such. It can hardly be otherwise since the concept of Divine Purpose is germane to my constructive schema as a whole, and is not merely tacked on at the end to justify my posing as a Gifford Lecturer.

I append a list of sundry publications, in which I have said some things which supplement what I have set down in the pages that follow. There are a few sentences which have been transferred from the former to the latter.

That there are passages in these *parerga*, and in the pages of *Emergent Evolution*, which stand sorely in need of revision goes without saying. Even as I pass the final proofs of these lectures I call to mind Huxley's saying, that a book of his never came hot from the press without his wishing to re-write it.

C. LLOYD MORGAN.

BRISTOL, *September* 1925.

LIST OF PUBLICATIONS referred to on p. xiv

Chapter on " Biology " in *Evolution in the Light of Modern Knowledge* (Blackie, 1925).

" Naturalisme et Vie," *Scientia*, July 1925.

" Processes of Life and Mind," Huxley, Centenary Supplement, *Nature*, 9th May 1925.

" Optical Records and Relativity," *Nature*, 18th Oct. 1924.

" Emergent Evolution," *Mind*, vol. xxxiv., N.S. No. 133, 1924.

" The Conditioned Response," Long Fox Lecture, *Bristol Med Chi. Journ.*, 1924.

" Autonomy of Life and Mind," *The Modern Churchman*, September 1924.

" A Philosophy of Evolution," in *Contemp. British Phil.* (Allen and Unwin, 1924).

" Instinctive Behaviour and Experience," *Brit. Journ. of Psych.* (General Section), vol. xii., part i., June 1921.

" Psychical Selection : Expression and Impression," *ibid.*, vol. xi., January 1921.

" Spencer's Philosophy of Science," Herbert Spencer Lecture, *Oxf. Clar. Press*, 1913.

" A Garden of Ethics," *International Journ. of Ethics*, July 1911.

CONTENTS

PAGE

PREFACE vii

LECTURE I
CONCOMITANCE OF LIFE AND MIND
SECTION
1. Introductory 1
2. Unrestricted Concomitance 7
3. The Concept of Reference 13
4. The Concept of Enjoyment 19
5. Back to Spinoza ? 26

LECTURE II
BEHAVIOUR
6. Our Schema in Outline 31
7. Plain Tale of Behaviour 37
8. Interpretations of Plain Tale 43
9. Guidance, Trial, and Error 49
10. Trial and Error under Canon of Emergent Interpretation 56

LECTURE III
LIFE AS EMERGENT
11. Substantial and Determinate Plans . . 62
12. Mechanism and Monadism . . . 68
13. The Natural Origin of the Living . . 74
14. Concerning the Life-Plan . . . 80
15. The Concept of Hormism 87

xvii

LECTURE IV

A TURNING-POINT IN EVOLUTIONARY ADVANCE

SECTION PAGE
16. Patterns and the Engram. 94
17. Some Observation and an Interpretation . . . 100
18. Conditioned Behaviour 107
19. Bearing on the Story of Mind 112
20. Learning and Habit 119

LECTURE V

EMERGENCE IN MIND

21. Mind an Attribute of Nature 125
22. Levels of Reference 131
23. To What is the Word " Instinctive " Adjectival ? . 137
24. Instinctive Knowledge. Literary Psychology . . 143
25. Are there Instinctive Fore-plans ? 149

LECTURE VI

PLEASURE AND PAIN

26. Getting and Coming 156
27. The Push of Discomfort 162
28. Consonance of Welfare and Pleasure 168
29. Emotional Enjoyment 174
30. Foretaste in Enjoyment 180

LECTURE VII

FORE-PLANS OF ACTION

31. A Doctrine of Guidance 187
32. Guidance under Plan 192
33. Child and Boy 202
34. Subhuman Emergence of Plan in Mind . . . 206
35. Cortical Concomitants 214

LECTURE VIII

THOUGHT AND ACTION

SECTION   PAGE

36. The Story of Influence and of Reference . . . 218
37. Inclusion or Possession ? 224
38. The Evolution of Reference 231
39. Reference under Schema 238
40. In Search of Common Factors 244

LECTURE IX

SELF AND OTHERS

41. The Self of Enjoyment 250
42. The Self for Contemplation 256
43. Value and Worth 261
44. A Social Episode 265
45. From Pleasure through Joy to Love 272

LECTURE X

DIVINE PURPOSE

46. Plan and Purpose 279
47. A Religious Attitude 284
48. Reality of Divine Purpose 293
49. The Spiritual and the Supernatural 299
50. God as Spiritual Substance 306

INDEX 314

LECTURE I

CONCOMITANCE OF LIFE AND MIND

§ 1. *Introductory*

IF one accept a naturalistic interpretation not only of inorganic events, but of those events which we group under the headings of life and of mind, can one still believe that all these events are manifestations of Divine Purpose? I, for one, can and do accept the most thorough-going naturalism. I, for one, still retain, and am confirmed in, my belief in God.

My thorough-going naturalism takes form in the concept of evolution as emergent and universally applicable throughout nature, including human nature, bodily and mental. But I am one of those who hold that life and mind should not be identified with, but should be distinguished from, spirit. I regard life and mind as manifestations of spirit in an ascending hierarchy of such manifestations. This brings them within the orbit of natural events to be interpreted subject to the methods of naturalism. In accordance with this view, spirit is not a " quality " at the summit of the evolutionary hierarchy. It is that of which *all* qualities, from lowest to highest, are manifestations under the conditions of " time and space."

1

Hence, in the earlier part of this course, my aim will be to develop a naturalistic interpretation of the evolutionary advance of life and mind. Save for some incidental reference on a few occasions, I shall reserve till my concluding lecture that which is for me the most important of all issues, namely, Is the concept of emergent evolution inconsistent with belief in Divine Purpose ?

It was Lord Gifford's wish that the lecturers under his trust should " treat their subject as a purely natural science." I may at least claim that my avenue of approach purports to be scientific ; for if naturalism be not rooted in science it has no status as a contribution to philosophy.

Each man of science in his special province of inquiry deals with events which run their course in ascertainable ways. They go together in orderly clusters. Any such cluster within which the relations of events are intrinsic, or within it, constitutes a natural entity—for example, an atom, a crystal, an organism ; and in virtue of the intrinsic relations of its constituent events any such entity exhibits certain distinguishable qualities. But these entities are set in relational fields. Here the inter-relations between them severally are extrinsic ; and in virtue of its extrinsic relations to other natural entities, each exhibits certain distinguishable properties.

Events, then, and natural clusters of events as entities, behave in ascertainable ways. These ways the man of science, each within his province of inquiry, describes in sundry instances of their occurrence, and interprets as existent examples of some subsistent plan. Now this, that, or the other man of science seeks to interpret *some* events or integral clusters of events—those which fall within his special province. He is not concerned to essay the increasingly difficult task of surveying the whole kingdom of nature and seeking to interpret it in accordance with scientific method. One who does so, attempts to formulate in broad outline the generic and still determinate plan of advance in *all* natural entities. The outcome is a naturalistic interpretation.

Is it then claimed that in this varied world there is always evolutionary advance from lower and less complex entities—each an integral system of events —to those which are higher and more complex on the same path of advance? By no means. There is also the reverse process of dissolution with degradation of higher entities to lower. Take the atomic series. The evolutionary path of advance is, let us say, from the atom of hydrogen to that of uranium. Under dissolution the path of degradation is from uranium downwards. Both processes —ascending and descending—are abundantly illustrated in all provinces within the kingdom of nature. To emphasise the one does not entail denial of the other.

Is there always either ascending evolution or descending degradation? I think we may perhaps say that any given *integral entity* stands at a halting-stage on the upward or downward path. At this stage it may be regarded as a persistent eddy of events. But much of the world is composed (1) of relatively loose events not yet tied up in entities of integral status ; (2) of like events which have *plexity* of stuff, it is better not to speak of complexity in substance. I prefer to speak of *richness* in substance as correlated with complexity of stuff.

Now, obviously, there can be no substance without stuff, for that would mean going together with nothing to go together. It may be said, however, that there can be stuff without substance. But if we realise that we are dealing with some *integral entity* it should be clear that *its* stuff (the items that do go together) is strictly correlative with *its* substance. The word "stuff" covers the multiplicity of items that coexist in substantial unity. Cut out one electron from the nitrogen atom and you no longer have the substance or the stuff of that specific kind of atom.

It is worth while here to cast a passing glance at the probable attitude of the man of plain common sense. He may say: Now please drop your jargon about "integral entities" and the like; put the matter (if you can) less technically and more comprehensibly. Well, on these terms, I should ask him such a question as this. You hear a speech. Do you ever say: He talked a lot of stuff, but there was really no substance to it? If so, do you not mean that what you call the stuff—his words and the ideas they stood for—were irrelevant or did not hang together so as to form a coherent whole? That is just what I, too, mean by substance. But you may say that the stuff was there, more than enough of it. Yes; but it was quite irrelevant matter. Might you not yourself say: *That* is not the kind of stuff of which a substantial speech is made ? This means that it is not the stuff of a coherent whole, for you admit that there was no such whole. In other words, the stuff and substance of the coherent whole go hand in hand. I need not here pursue the matter any further. It must suffice to lay stress on the essential point— always discreteness and multiplicity of items of stuff ; always unity and indivisibility of substance in that which is worthy of the name of an integral entity.

§ 2. *Unrestricted Concomitance*

We have seen that the stress is to be on *integral entities*, and that emergent evolution deals with their *advance* in complexity of stuff and in richness of substantial unity.

I pass now to the concept of correlation or concomitance. In my first course of lectures and elsewhere I have used the word "correlation." As thus used it signifies an unique manner of co-existence of those different aspects of events which are commonly spoken of as physical and psychical. Such correlation is, I believe, ubiquitous and universal. But we shall only incidentally be concerned with its wider sweep ; for our province of inquiry is that of life and mind. Here it takes this form : There is no life without mind ; no mind save as correlated or concomitant with life-processes.

Now the word "psychical," the word "mind," and the word "correlation," are ambiguous. Each may be used in more than one sense. I seek, so far as is possible, to avoid ambiguity. To that end in what follows I shall not use the word "psychical."

But in *Emergent Evolution* I spoke of a "psychical system" that has not reached the status of a "mind." There the word "mind" denoted a psychical system in which "prospective reference" plays a distinctive part. If I drop the word "psychical" I can no longer use the word "mind" in this restricted sense. Henceforward I shall use it without any such restriction. If apology be due for this change of usage it is tendered.

In view of the ambiguity of the word "correlation" I shall drop that word also, and shall speak of the *concomitance* of physical and physiological processes with mental processes. I think this change of usage will conduce to clearness. I do not abandon the concept of correlation in a definable sense, but the word "concomitance" may serve to show more clearly what I mean.

On this understanding our hypothesis is that any given organism affords an instance of the fundamental duality in nature, spoken of by Spinoza as interpretable under two "attributes." The organism may be considered (1) in physiological regard in respect of its life ; or (2) in psychological regard in respect of its mind. Concomitance emphasises that which may be otherwise expressed : Never one attribute without the other. This does not preclude the belief that, underlying this two-fold expression in life and in mind, there is substantial unity common to both.

There is another word that gives endless trouble —namely, the word "conscious." Seeing how much is written nowadays on "consciousness and the unconscious" one can hardly drop it altogether.

But it is difficult to define and may perhaps be indefinable. It seems that when an act is spoken of as done consciously, this often implies that it is performed with conscious intent or under conscious guidance. But it sometimes implies only that the performance carries such and such mental concomitants, say in some sort of " feeling." I shall hereafter suggest (*cf.* Lecture V) that we may leave the context to decide in which of these two senses the word is used. Of course, in the latter and broader sense, all vital action is, on our hypothesis, conscious since it has mental concomitants of some kind. We have, however, to realise that a great number of people—perhaps the great majority of biologists— are not prepared to accept this hypothesis of un-restricted concomitance. They limit concomitance to certain processes that occur only in certain parts of the central nervous system. Among these was Huxley, who, in 1871, spoke of the concomitance of that which he spoke of as " psychosis " with " neurosis " (*Essays,* ii. 158, *cf.* i. 240).

Here again we are confronted with a verbal difficulty. Since both these words are now com-monly used with quite a different meaning, their retention would lead to misunderstanding. We must find or make some substitutes. The expression " mental events "—in the broad sense of the word " mental "—has little ambiguity. I ask leave to speak of the concomitant physiological events as *bioses*, and to distinguish the events within the central nervous system as *neuro-bioses*. Under un-restricted concomitance, then, mental events accom-pany all bioses. Under restricted concomitance, as advocated by Huxley, they accompany neuro-bioses only.

Now, with regard to mental events, the only direct and first-hand evidence of their occurrence is that they are " given in experience "—which means, I take it, that they exist as the items of stuff in some mind—yours or mine as the case may be.

But, rightly or wrongly, we attribute mental events to others on a basis of evidence which is necessarily indirect since we cannot ourselves verily feel what they feel, but only peradventure the like of it. Perhaps (again rightly or wrongly) we attribute something analogous to what we feel, or at any rate occurrences of that kind, to the sea anemone, or even to the amœba, on the basis of its observed behaviour. Here, however, there are no neuro-bioses, for there are no neurones to constitute a synaptic nervous system. But there are bioses. If, then, we do (1) attribute mind, of however lowly a rank, to such organisms as the infusoria, and (2) interpret in terms of concomitance, we pass from a restricted con-comitance of mental events with certain neuro-bioses of high rank in some specialised region of the brain (or organ of like function) to the much less restricted concomitance of mental events with bioses or life-occurrences of some sort. The further ques-tion then arises : Can we so differentiate bioses as to say : These bioses (say in some animals) are concomitant with mental events, but *those* bioses (say in plants) are not thus concomitant ? So far as I am aware we cannot do so with confidence. I am therefore prepared (until evidence to the contrary is forthcoming) to accept as a working hypothesis *unrestricted concomitance* of all bioses in an ascending order of rank with mental events in a corresponding order of rank.

The position then, so far, is this. Within the whole domain of those integral entities we call organisms there is concomitance of mental events with bioses—that is, physical and physiological events. But on the hypothesis of emergent evolution (1) the advance of natural events is from the lower and less complex and rich, to the higher and more complex and rich; (2) in any higher entity along the same line of advance occurrences of the lower order are not altogether ousted by those of the higher order, but are retained and still persist in such wise as to afford the natural foundations on which these occurrences of a higher order are built.

We must consider, therefore, what will be the joint outcome if both these hypotheses (emergent evolution and unrestricted concomitance) be accepted. We must regard a man, for example, (1) as an evolutionary product, subject (2) to unrestricted concomitance. He is a complex system of bioses ; he is also a complex system of mental events. If we retain for convenience Spinoza's " attributes " as meaning " in this regard or in that," then in life-regard he is a system of bioses, but in mind-regard he is a system of mental events. Substantially he is one being ; but he is physical (which here includes physiological) in one attribute, mental in the other.

Contrast now the hypothesis of unrestricted concomitance with that of restricted concomitance. According to the latter, as advocated by Huxley and still widely accepted, what is felt in experiencing

is felt only in the *sensorium*. Here and here only
(say in some part of the upper brain) does concomitance obtain. From what, then, do neuro-bioses
arise in evolutionary genesis ? They arise from
other, less specialised, bioses within the same attribute—that is, in biological regard. And from what do
the concomitant mental events arise in evolutionary
genesis ? To this question the answer under the
restricted hypothesis is : We do not know. They
just do arise when the physiological level of neuro-
bioses is reached. Of their evolutionary genesis
we must frankly confess our ignorance. On the
unrestricted hypothesis they are in due course
emergent in the ascending development of a mind
of high status.

Let it then be understood clearly that the hypothesis of unrestricted concomitance does *not* imply
that occurrences in either attribute emerge from
occurrences in the other. The hypothesis is that
from the very beginning, so far as we can descry it,
mind is concomitant with life. This hypothesis that
concomitance obtains in respect of *all bioses* throughout the living body does not, I submit, run counter
to common-sense notions ; for the plain man often
says that some emotional thrill that he experiences
involves nearly every fibre of his tingling body. It
was long ago advocated by G. H. Lewes, who urged
" that the sensorium is the whole sensible organism
and not any one isolated portion of it " (*Physical
Basis of Mind*, p. 440). It is the whole life-system that
is, in the phrase then current, " the organ of mind."

If a very primitive mind be attributed to the uni-
cellular amœba, on what grounds should it *not* be

attributed severally to all the cells of the multi-cellular organism, (*a*) so far as bioses (life-changes) occur in them, and (*b*) on the understanding that the concomitant mental events are integrated in the mind just as the bioses are integrated in the body? (2) Since the adult organism is developed from a fertilised ovum, may not the adult mind be developed from mental events concomitant with bioses in that ovum? This, it may be said, is not only speculative but goes far beyond the evidence. But is it an inference that is *contradicted* by the evidence? And may we not here revert to (1) above and ask: If lowly mind be attributed to the paramœcium, on what grounds should it *not* be attributed to the fertilised ovum?

§ 3. *The Concept of Reference*

Thus far I have stated the case for unrestricted concomitance in life and mind. It is, however, clear that acceptance of concomitance in this unrestricted form does not preclude restricted concomitance of mental events, specific in kind, with certain physiological events which are also of some specific kind —such as " neuro-bioses " in the brain. All the evidence points that way.

We have now to consider mental events. It is part of my thesis that they may be distinguished under two headings—(1) " enjoyment " and (2) " reference," cognitive or reflective. I shall deal with enjoyment in the next section. In this section I shall try to make clear what I mean by reference, and to show how it plays a part at different stages in the development of a mind.

First, however, something further must be said with respect to the story of life which accompanies the story of mind. The story of life is always that of what broadly speaking may be called physical *influence* and action consequent thereon. It has been well said : " The entire life of any organism consists of a series of responses to stimuli which reach it from various sources " (A. Dendy). Here one must emphasise the concept of substantial unity in the life as a whole—that which comprises multifarious bioses as items of stuff. But of each several biosis it is still true that it is what it is in response to stimulation. Any change that occurs in it is due to some physical or biochemical influence. This, at any given moment, may be traceable (1) to some external source from which stimulation comes to some part of the organism which is specially receptive thereof ; or (2) to some internal source in other current bioses. And when it is traceable to some internal source there is often re-excitation, by an indirect course within the body, of the same kind of change as was initially traceable to direct stimulation from an external source. Under such re-excitation we have what may appropriately be called " physiological revival" of a change like to that which was in the first instance traceable to some specific kind of direct stimulation. It is a complex story ; and we shall hereafter learn some of its details. Here and now it must suffice to lay stress on two points : first, that it is throughout a story of influence received and of response thereto ; and, secondly, that there is ample provision for physiological revival.

In passing to the mind-story we are on what for most people is much more familiar ground. Not only is it familiar ground since much of it is trodden in our daily experience, but our mental steps in traversing it are readily described in terms of common speech. Hence some resentment may be felt at the introduction of more technical phraseology. But for those who wish to dig a little below the surface, it is worth while to face such technicalities as may serve to make the position clear.

I ask, first, to draw a radical distinction between " influence "—by which I mean physical influence—which is germane to the life-story, and " reference "—by which I mean something purely mental as part of the mind-story.

Let us, then, consider what happens when we are in relation to the external world. From things or events at a distance, close by, or even in contact with our bodies, influence comes in so as to take effect on our bodily life ; but reference goes forth from the mind to that from which the body receives influence. Thus a distant star influences the retina of my eye ; thereupon there is reference from my mind to Sirius. One may say, somewhat picturesquely, that *influence comes in to* the eye while reference *goes forth from the mind* that is concomitant with the physiological processes due to this influence. But the coming of influence from Sirius takes time in transmission ; whereas reference is instantaneous. If then one speaks, picturesquely, of reference as " going forth," it must not be supposed that anything travels from the mind to Sirius, as object of reference, in the same kind of physical way that light-influence travels from the star to the eye. It is this that, in part at least, marks the radical distinction between influence and reference.

Now just as the life-story tells of the evolutionary processes and products of physical influence, so does the mind-story tell of the progressive evolution of reference. In each story we pass from lower to higher stages in the course of emergent advance. But whereas in telling the life-story we commonly proceed upwards from lower and earlier stages—say in the individual life-history—to higher and later stages, in trying to read the mind-story we more conveniently start from the high level to which, as adults, we have ourselves attained, and then work down to lower levels perhaps better illustrated in the child-mind, or the animal-mind.

We shall have, later on, to consider what I speak of as evolutionary levels of reference at greater length and in further detail. It must here suffice briefly to indicate what characterises three main levels of reference.

The highest is that of *reflective reference*. Here we have such reference as there may be in your mind or mine, on some given occasion, to European politics, to Elizabethan literature, to the Einstein theory, to one's plan for a summer holiday, for a business letter we have to write, for some experiment we wish to try. Under reflective reference there is mental rehearsal of events conjured up under intentional revival or recall. How such schematic plans take form we cannot now stay to consider. The point here is that this is a kind of reference that we do not attribute to quite little children or to animals.

Below this reflective reference is what I shall speak of as *cognitive reference*. This we find not only underlying the higher kind of reference in ourselves, but itself in evidence in all intelligent animals. It is that which chiefly distinguishes the animal-mind. In such cognitive reference, in us as in them, there is always mental revival in the form of imagery or of practical meaning for behaviour. This supplements, and forms what James called a fringe to, that which is directly given in sensory acquaintance under stimulation. We see, for example, a piece of ice and say that it " looks " cold, and hard, and slippery. What is here given in sensory acquaintance is visual ; but we have learnt to expect that, under suitable behaviour, coldness, hardness, and slipperiness will be given. That which *will* be given, and *is* expected, is referred to the piece of ice which thus becomes an object of cognitive reference. Under such reference animals and children learn through behaving, and behave more and more appropriately through learning. All true " location in space " is learnt under cognitive reference.

It is generally conceded that, concomitant with the several items of imagery in mental revival, there are physiological events. But under cognitive reference there is *meaning* in expectant prevision. And it is again, and again, and yet again, roundly asserted that there is no physiological concomitant of meaning. I think that this assertion, when it is more fully expanded, comes to this : There may be physiological concomitants of this or that imaginal item, but there is no such concomitant of their all going together in substantial unity. Our contention

2

is that " substance " is common to both. The
bioses go together in substantial unity, and only in
so far as they do so is there one life in the organism.
The mental events likewise go together in the
substantial unity of meaning ; and only in so far
as they do so is there cognitive reference on the part
of one mind.

As the outcome of cognitive reference there is,
then, at any given time, an integral synthesis com-
prising an interrelated group of mental events with
substantial unity of meaning for current behaviour.
But each item of stuff was, prior to such synthesis,
initially independent of the others under concomit-
tance with some specific mode of external influence.
We must, therefore, apply the method of distin-
guishing analysis. Under such analysis we concentrate attention on *any one item of stuff* as first
given in direct sensory acquaintance—in vision, in
hearing, in touch, in taste, or smell, and so forth.
There is here as yet no meaning, for that comes in
substantial synthesis under cognitive reference. Is
there, then, in respect of each several item of stuff,
no reference ? My contention is that, even here, on
receipt of influence, reference goes forth. If it do
not, how does reference begin in the individual
mind ? May it not be correlative with the very
first touch of influence from without ? But, if so,
it is not cognitive reference, for there is, as yet, no
relevant revival and no meaning. Let me call it
non-cognitive reference. It is exemplified in hundreds
of ways at the outset of sensory acquaintance with
things and events. It is basal since all cognitive
reference is founded thereon.

Now follows a little bit of purely speculative hypothesis, which is, however, cardinal to my constructive schema. I put it in abstract form with the utmost brevity.

In physical and physiological regard there is (1) influence of one entity on another, let us say of e on m. In mental regard there is (2) reference from concomitant μ to ϵ. It has been a long and difficult business to learn how best to tell a comprehensive story in which any instance under (1) has its place in a schema of all other instances of physical influence with action and reaction throughout nature. No less long and difficult a business is it to learn how best to tell how any instance under (2) has its place in a schema of all other such instances of reference in any personal mind (cf. §§ 38, 39).

Even so the task remains to bring these two stories into relation in such wise as to enable us to interpret conscious guidance of behaviour and conduct under cognitive and reflective reference.

§ 4. *The Concept of Enjoyment*

In the story of mind reference " goes forth " or is projicient. But such objective reference does not exhaust the story of mind ; for if in the course of mental development its outcome is something mind*ed*, there is also the correlative outcome—namely, some-one mind*ing*. It is to this " someone " that we must now direct reflective attention.

In some sense of the expression, the someone who minds—let us say with objective reference to something minded—does so " *with enjoyment*." What do I mean and ask others to understand by enjoyment? Professor Alexander and I both use this word, taken over from common speech and adapted as a technical term; but our usage and the implications of such usage are not quite the same. There is, however, much in common; and such difference as there is may serve to throw sidelights on the question—which many will raise—whether the concept thus labelled has validity or value for purposes of interpretation. Here and now it is *my* usage that I must try to render comprehensible.

The word is taken over from popular speech. How is it there used? One may say that one sees with enjoyment the view from a hill-top. Here that to which cognitive reference goes forth is the landscape; and in our common elliptical phraseology one may speak of enjoying the view. Taken literally this goes far to annul any distinction; for what we cognise that also we enjoy. The landscape may be spoken of as the object of enjoyment. Still what we mean, I think, is that one enjoys *seeing* the view. But one also enjoys *breathing* the fresh air, *tingling* with healthy exercise, *appreciating* the comments of one's companion, and so forth. And all these go together in the someone that then and there one *is*. It seems, then, that under cognitive reference we get the view as seen, and that under enjoyment we get seeing the view, *and much else*.

Of course, we commonly take the " much else " for granted; but, apart from it, would one be the someone that one is when one sees the view? Under reference, cognitive or reflective, we single out the specific somewhat to which this reference goes forth. No doubt correlative with this *item of reference*—one among many, for there is also reference to the balmy air, and "much else"—there is an *item of enjoyment* in the someone concerned. But *how* one enjoys, then and there, comprises *all* the items of enjoyment that go together substantially at the time-being.

That shifts the emphasis on to the "how" in enjoying. Let us grant that we can in some fashion —difficult enough—describe our enjoyment. Then, I suppose, that most people will say that what characterises any kind of enjoyment is that it is pleasant or agreeable. Now I ask that if the word be used, as I suggest, for interpretative purposes, this feature, important as it is, may be left out of account. That means a broadening of the connotation of the technical term so as to include either agreeable or disagreeable enjoyment. This may seem an outrage to common sense. But people have grown accustomed to "acceleration" as either positive (speeding up), or negative (slowing down), or even mere change of direction. They may soon grasp that, as we use the term, enjoyment may so change as to be relatively positive (agreeable) or negative (disagreeable). We need *one* word for that which may carry either positive or negative signature. I can find no better term than enjoyment.

So far, on the hill-top in view of the prospect, there is cognitive reference, and there is enjoyment —inseparable, but I think distinguishable. Suppose, however, that one feels "fit" or "out of sorts." There is enjoyment. Is there *cognitive* reference? No doubt if we think about it, and ask ourselves

organism is central in the give and take of influence. Life still implies *intrinsic* relations within the organism ; but it finds expression in behaviour which implies *extrinsic* relations between the organism and its environment. Within the organism the items of stuff in relation are bioses or physiological events. In an intelligible sense these items are severally lived ; but only in so far as they go together in substantial unity is there a living organism as one integral whole.

Pass now to mind as concomitant with life. Here again intrinsic relations should be distinguished from extrinsic relations. As thus distinguished enjoyment is the integral set of intrinsic relations. Under a cognitive reference we have the extrinsic relatedness commonly spoken of as that of the mind to its object. Broadly speaking the objective field to which reference goes forth plays in mental regard the part that the physical environment plays in biological regard, and the going forth of reference is more or less closely in accord with the output of behaviour. Such accord is the outcome of evolution.

In respect of mind, therefore, the question arises : What are we to understand by the expression " in mind ? " Are we to include only intrinsic relations in enjoyment—that is, all the varied modes of minding including feeling fit and the like ? Or are we to include also that which is objectively minded—say under cognitive reference ? Professor Alexander takes the former view. For him, as I understand, what is in mind and constitutive of mind is enjoyment and enjoyment

only. All that is objective under what I call cognitive reference (of which he renders a new-realistic
account quite different from that which I can
accept) is distinctly non-mental.

Accepting as I do in the present context the more
comprehensive concept of life, I accept also the more
comprehensive concept of mind. In other words,
I take the expression " in mind " to include what
Berkeley spoke of as there " by way of idea " as well
as that which is distinguishable as there " by way
of attribute."   Hence for me there are in mind (*a*)
intrinsic enjoyment, and (*b*) the projicient outcome
of extrinsic reference, cognitive or reflective.

Here and now intrinsic enjoyment is in focus.
The question was raised : What is enjoyed when
someone is enjoying ?   I submit that in an intelligible
sense one may reply : The several items of constituent stuff are enjoy*ed*; but enjoy*ing* is the substantial unity in someone, or in some mind, however
lowly in status.   Enjoyment comprises multifarious
items of stuff. One of these which has emphasis at
some time—being is reflectively singled out—say,
seeing the view from the hill-top. Then we say :
This—among many other items—was enjoyed. But
it was enjoyed by someone—say, by me. What,
then, am I? Someone other than the enjoyment
I call mine ? Nay ; intrinsically I *am*, in mental
regard, the emergent synthesis of all the items of
stuff, severally enjoyed, subject always to substantial unity in enjoying.

But within the interpenetrating synthesis of enjoying I believe that the several items of stuff—seeing
the view, breathing the fresh air, tingling with

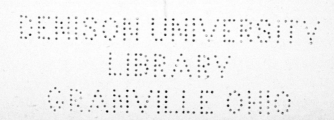

DENISON UNIVERSITY
LIBRARY
GRANVILLE OHIO

exercise, feeling fit, appreciating the comments of my companion, and the rest—have each a quality of enjoyment all its own. Here my concept of the intrinsic nature of enjoyment—as through and through, from first to last, subject to difference in quality—differs, as I understand, from that of Mr Alexander.

§ 5. *Back to Spinoza?*

" Most writers on the emotions and on human conduct," said Spinoza, " seem to be treating rather of matters outside nature than of natural phenomena." Not so did he treat of them. And here my cry is : Back to Spinoza. Does this mean that I too " shall consider human actions and desires in exactly the same manner as though I were concerned with lines, planes, and solids " ? Not so, unless in accordance with the trend of his teaching we may translate " geometrically " into the wider concept to which " naturalistically " now gives expression. In any case we must treat them subject to emergence. When I say : Back to Spinoza, I mean : Back to the foundations laid by Spinoza on which may be built a new superstructure that incorporates a concept of evolution unknown in this day. We must paraphrase his statement and say : Our aim is to treat all mental events, including all modes of human perception and thought, and all modes of human emotion, in exactly the same manner as though we were concerned with any other instances of advance within the plan of emergent evolution. In brief, mind no less than life, and life no less than atomicity or molecularity, fall within the emergent schema.

DENISON UNIVERSITY
LIBRARY
GRANVILLE OHIO

Since I owe a debt to Spinoza I feel called on to say a few words in its discharge. But since (1) I make no pretence to exact scholarship ; since (2) I am here concerned only with that part of his thought which deals with what I call concomitance ; and since (3) I may read into his teaching closer accord with my own views than the text of the *Ethics*, taken as a whole, warrants ; it will be better to raise questions as to what he sought to convey in the language of his time, than to presume to do more than express a tentative opinion as to what the answers should be.

Spinoza says, for example : " The object of the idea constituting the human mind is the body " (Pt. ii. Prop. 23). If I paraphrase thus : " The object (that is, ' a certain mode of extension ') which is the physical concomitant of the *enjoyment* which constitutes the human mind is the living body," would Spinoza accept or reject this reading of his thought ?

Again, when Spinoza says : " By affection or emotion I mean the modification of the body whereby the active power of the said body is increased or diminished, aided or constrained, and also *the ideas of such modification* " (Pt. iii. Def. 3), may I substitute for the words in italics " the enjoyment which is the mental concomitant of such modifications " ?

I surmise that Spinoza might reply, " Yes, that is part of my meaning, but it is by no means all that I wish to convey ; for it empties the word ' idea ' of all distinctively cognitive reference, and that is far from the import of my teaching as a whole." May we then take what I speak of as concomitant enjoyment as *part* of the connotation of the word

" idea " in Spinoza's usage ?   If so we shall expect
to find difference of emphasis on this part and on
that in different passages.   Is it this part rather
than the cognitive part that receives emphasis when
Spinoza says that " a mode of extension and the
idea of that mode are one and the same though
expressed in two ways " (ii. 7, note) ; and that this
must be taken as " applying not more to men than
to other individual things, all of which, though in
different degrees, are animated " (ii. 13, note) ?

I take it that all might agree that it is part of
Spinoza's teaching that, as " expressed in two ways,"
neither can cause any change in the other—that there
can be no interaction of modes of expression.   Hence
(here I will venture again to paraphrase Spinoza)
(1) so long as we consider events as physical modes
we must interpret the whole of nature in terms of
physical action only ; and (2) so long as we consider
events as mental modes we must interpret the whole
of nature in terms of mental reference only.   These
clauses do not present alternatives—this or that—
one to be accepted and the other rejected.   They
are complementary.   This supplies what that lacks.
In Spinoza's seventh proposition (Pt. ii.) they are
united.   The " order and connection of ideas is the
same as the order and connection of things."   Whatever else this may mean, may we substitute as *part*
of its meaning : The evolutionary advance of mental
events is interpretable on the same principles as
that of physical events ?   Such is the teaching of emergent evolution.   I think Spinoza might look kindly
upon it.

I even venture to hope that he might look not

unkindly on some such paraphrase as this : The order and connection of mental events, say in man, expresses in one attribute *the same substantial unity* as the order and connection of physiological events expresses in the other attribute.

In any case Spinoza clearly realised that, under reflective inquiry, bodily expression is a guiding clue to inference with respect to mental expression. He says : " In order to determine wherein the human mind differs from other things, and wherein it surpasses them, it is necessary for us to know the nature of its [concomitant] object, that is, of the human body " (ii. 13, sch.).

It may be said that I unwarrantably insert in brackets the word " concomitant "—whereas Spinoza probably meant the body as an object of cognitive reference. I submit that he may have meant both.

Be that as it may, we must now turn to the cognitive part of the connotation of the word " idea." Take first this cardinal proposition " The human mind perceives no external body save through ideas of the modifications of its own body " (ii. ? 26). I submit that here it is open to us still to lay stress on that which I speak of as concomitance. No percept, we may say, without such and such bodily concomitants of our enjoyment in perceiving. But in the second corollary of the sixteenth proposition Spinoza says " that the ideas we have of external bodies indicate rather the constitution of our own body than the constitution of external bodies." Here it seems quite clear that the emphasis is cognitive. The emphasis is not on enjoyment in perceiving, which has its concomitant in some brain-process

Since it is part of my aim to distinguish life and mind from Spirit I seek also to use distinctive words. Hence I speak of " manifestations " of Spirit. But Spirit is nowise separable from life and mind, nor they from it. What is given for reflective contemplation is a world-plan of natural events. I hold that this world-plan is a manifestation of Divine Purpose. We human folk are, in life and mind, integral parts of that world-plan. We too are manifestations of Spirit which is " revealed " within us. Each of us *is* a life, a mind, and Spirit—an instance of life as one expression of world-plan, of mind as a different expression of that world-plan, of Spirit in so far as the Substance of that world-plan is revealed within us. The world-plan, through and through, from its lowest to its highest expression, is manifestation of God ; in you and me—in each of us severally— God as Spirit is partially revealed. This revelation is only partial since each of us is only an individual instance of that which in full manifestation is universal.

Keeping here and now to life and mind as expressions of world-plan, under duality of nature, each is inseparably concomitant with the other. And there is a valid sense in which it may be said that intrinsically neither its life nor its mind passes beyond the confines of this or that embodied and enminded entity. But in respect of its life it is, as we acknowledge, extrinsically in relation to multifarious physical events around it. From the action of these it is in receipt of influence ; on them it has influence in the reaction of behaviour. So, too, in respect of its mind. It is not only a system of intrinsic enjoyment; it is also in extrinsic relation to an objective world around it through reference, first non-cognitive, later cognitive, in due course reflective, in natural order of advance.

As expressions of world-plan life and mind, each in its several regard, afford, as I think, illustrations of emergent evolution along lines of advance towards further complexity in the stuff of events and towards increasing richness in substantial unity. Progressive advance in evolution is here my theme; and I submit that it is irrelevant to say that, under retrogressive dissolution, there is also, and often concurrently, a reversal of natural progress in regress no less natural. No doubt there is. And it may be that in life and mind there are always both, in subtly changing equipoise. But it is the salient feature in *progress* that I seek to elucidate.

It should, however, clearly be understood that unrestricted concomitance and the emergence of new qualities are two quite distinct concepts. Spinoza could advocate the one long before the other had been thought of. No less clearly should it be understood that, distinct from either concomitance or emergence, is the concept of reference as that which in mental regard is the reciprocal counterpart of influence in physical regard. Why this should be so—nay more, why there should be either influence or reference in the realm of nature—I know not. Both are given. My hypothesis is that each is correlative to the other in the evolution of life and mind.

These three concepts—unrestricted concomitance,

3

emergence as the keynote of progress, and reference as correlative with influence—each of which may be accepted or rejected independently of the others, are knit together in the schema that I advocate. Thus combined in one synthesis they contribute, as I think, to its substantial unity.

The schema as it is here offered for consideration and criticism is frankly naturalistic. But, for me, this means only that it deals with nature as we find it. My belief is that, apart from God, that which we call the realm of nature would have neither being nor evolutionary becoming. But, quite irrespective of such belief, I contend that naturalism as such (if we talk in terms of *isms*) remains quite unaffected. The natural realm is what it is, and as it is, whether its being and its progress be further explained in terms other than naturalistic, or left unexplained.

None the less it follows from concomitance that the mental and the physical events in any given organism belong to *one natural realm*. Avowedly, therefore, the hypothesis I advocate is alternative to that of interaction of entities belonging to two disparate realms of being.

Taking the latter hypothesis in one of its forms, permit me to speak of it as *animism*. Then animism is antithetical to naturalism. According to animism mental processes are not unrestrictedly concomitant with bodily events, but belong to a disparate entity that has being independently of the body which it controls. If we speak of this as the mind, it enters into possession of the body, using its sense-organs as instruments of reception and its motor organs as

executive instruments. Animism implies what Mr
Johnson speaks of as impartial dualism, whereas
naturalism implies duality in attribute.

And what of the soul ? Cardinal to the animistic
hypothesis is the " anima " as belonging to a realm
of being disparate from the physical realm to which
the mechanism of the body, as such, belongs. This
anima is spoken of sometimes as life, sometimes as
mind, sometimes as spirit. If the word " soul "
be still used in this context it is, I suppose, synony-
mous with anima. There are, however, many
dualists who would say that soul should be distinguished from life. They would not speak of the
soul of a plant. There are others who would say
that though we can properly speak of the soul of
man we should not speak of the soul of a cow or a
guinea-pig. The word clearly needs careful definition, or at least adjectival qualification. Some
might, for example, distinguish the rational soul of
man as something more than mind and perhaps
something less than spirit.

In any case what is currently understood by
" the soul-theory " has its roots in dualism. And
what some people mean when they speak of " a
psychology without a soul " is a psychology other
than dualistic. On these terms the advocate of
concomitance is precluded from using the word
within his thesis. There is, however, a sense in
which he may, under suitable definition, speak of
the soul as distinctive of that level of mental development at which a *concept* of Spirit is within the
field of reflective reference. In that sense it ear-
marks an important step upwards in the evolution

of mind. But in that sense it carries no dualistic implications.

Here, and elsewhere later on, it is impossible to indicate the nature of the hypothesis of duality in attribute, in aspect, in expression, in diverse regard, or however otherwise it may be stated, without indicating also the nature of the dualistic hypothesis, whether it take the guise of animism or some other guise. I am concerned to say what I can in support of the former. But let it not be supposed that I regard or would speak of the latter, and those who support it, with disrespect. The issue raised is no doubt controversial ; it is in close touch with deep-seated convictions. Let each party state clearly the evidence as he reads it, and set forth the arguments he relies on in favour of his thesis. Let him weigh the evidence and criticise the arguments brought forward by others. But let neither party speak of the other as " obsessed by this or that dogma "—whatever this may mean—or use words in a sense intended as opprobrious. It can serve no useful purpose to descend from the platform of recognised good manners in serious controversy.

One further implication of the interpretative schema I advocate is this. In the realm of natural events as they run their course in some given organism on a world-plan we seek to discover, there is, we contend, duality of expression in attribute. On the one hand there is physical and physiological expression to be dealt with in terms of action under influence—by which I mean, here and henceforward, physical and physiological action and influence. On the other hand, there is mental expression to be dealt with in terms of enjoyment and of reference. Thus of any such sequence of events two stories may be told, a life-story and a mind-story. But *as stories* neither can interact on the other; "this" aspect of the natural events themselves can in no wise interact with "that" aspect.

It may then be asked : How, on this hypothesis, can mental reference count in the guidance of events, as it assuredly does in many forms of animal behaviour and in all forms of human conduct ? The answer we shall give turns on the evolutionary story of reference when some *prevision* of that which is coming is concomitant with some *present* mode of action in the life-story, implying influence received under external stimulation and given back in behaviour.

§ 7. *Plain Tale of Behaviour*

In entering on more detailed consideration of life and mind we have to start somewhere. Let us begin with such behaviour as is exemplified by the lower organisms.

We must agree at the outset to use the word "behaviour" in some definite sense. For us, behaviour is a mode of bodily action. It falls within the story of life. Others—and quite justifiably under suitable definition—speak of mental behaviour ; we do not ; though of course, for us, in all instances of behaving there is concomitant accompaniment in enjoyment and in objective reference.

May we further agree provisionally and for the present to use the word behaviour for some describable performance of an organism as a whole in relation to its environment ? One does, no doubt, sometimes speak of the behaviour of the heart, of the salivary glands, and so on. But to cover all this we have the expression " functional action." Let us then reserve the word " behaviour " for that which an organism—a dog, or an amœba, or even a plant—does, or how it " acts," in this situation or that. The distinction is drawn only for convenience of treatment here and now.

Such whole-action behaviour is responsive. But so, in a broad sense, is all part-action within the animal or the plant. It has been said, for example, that the entire life of an organism consists of a series of responses to stimuli, external or internal. We may, however, at least provisionally, distinguish the responsive act as a whole to which partial responses are contributory.

It is characteristic of organisms that they are delicately sensitive to certain kinds of physical influence within a range of air-waves, for example, or of electromagnetic pulses, to which approximate limits can be assigned ; characteristic, too, that there has been, in the course of evolution, differentiation of receptivity for varied kinds of physical influence. As the outcome of reception the course of physiological action throughout the organism is in some measure changed. The effects of the reception of physical influence may, however, spread along definite channels which are thus differentiated as lines of *intervenient events within the organism*. And the effects of these intervenient events are further changes under which the organism

is said to respond to influence of this kind or that.
We have then reception, transmission, and response.

But where does all this obtain ? In the organism ;
at or within its confines. To what, then, does the
organism respond ? To the physical influence which
it receives under contact, or from beyond its confines,
through influence transmitted from a distance.
Take, in illustration, the plants that turn light-
wards in a cottager's window. To what do they
respond ? Is it to the sun as a source of radiation ?
Under the interpretation of a reflective observer,
Yes. In strictness, No. They respond then and
there to the influence that is received. And not
only in such an instance of plant-life, but in all
responsive behaviour, as such, that to which the
organism responds is not to a thing at a distance,
but to some physical influence received at home.

This may seem rather technical. But does it not
lead to the distinction—surely not unimportant—
between the behaviour itself, that which evokes it,
and what follows from behaving ?

With regard to the behaviour itself, as observable
performance on the part of some organism, it is
convenient to speak of its *form*. Thus in a water-
bird there is difference in form, in walking, running,
swimming, and diving, though many of the same
muscle-groups are in functional action in all of
them. *Form* in this sense is the visible expression
of the way in which a number of items of " stuff "
go together in " substance " so as to render behaviour
a recognisable whole. Here we may compare what
we call "good form" in the cricketer or the
golfer.

When one surveys the vast collection of instances of behaviour presented for our study, one may classify them either (a) under specific forms, or (b) in view of this or that outcome of the behaviour. The former classification is based on direct observation at the time-being. Thus and there does a bird, let us say, behave at successive phases of its life-history between immigration and emigration. The male, for example, occupies a territory; it behaves therein in describable ways; it effectively pairs; a nest is built; eggs are laid; incubation follows; the young are hatched; they are fed, and protected; parents and offspring depart to the South. Here our primary aim is to get the observable facts. Forms of behaviour readily distinguishable, some of them quite new to the individual under observation, are in evidence. These we classify under specific forms, and compare with those that are observed with a difference in the life-history of other animals. They constitute a series of acts in recognisable, but not necessarily invariable, order of sequence.

But one who thus observes and describes, compares and classifies, may not, and seldom does, therewith rest content. He seeks to go a step further, thus passing from (a) to (b). He asks: What is the observable outcome of this or that act? To what does it lead? He regards the successive acts as " links in a chain."

On direct observation may be founded not only particular statements of what is done by this or that individual bird (let us say) on some given occasion, but generalised statements of what such birds do in normal life-routine. We have under (*a*) description of this or that act, and under (*b*) the place of such an act in a natural plan of sequence. This is a step towards interpretation. One can say : Take any three acts in due order of sequence—say *l*, *m*, *n*—then, in normal routine, *l* is precedent to *m*, and *n* is consequent on *m*.

A further step introduces the external conditions of this or that act. This implies receipt of influence and response thereto. The position then is : We find that *l*, *m*, *n*, run their course in accordance with a " precedent and consequent plan " ; *but* subject to such response as is concurrently due to stimulation received from outside.

Now if we go no further than this we get what may be called a plain tale of behaviour. Let me give three examples.

1. Embed a bean in suitable soil. The tough skin bursts and the " cotyledons " open out. In one direction a shoot grows upwards, reaches open air and light, becomes green, and produces leaves. In the other direction a root grows downwards into deeper soil. According to the position of the bean the growth may be straight forward or take a curved course. We may speak of the eventual directions of shoot and root as towards and away from the light. But in plain tale we must realise that the bean in opaque soil is not subject to the influence of light-waves. Or we may speak of these directions as " geotropic "—" negative " in shoot, " positive " in root—under " gravitative attraction." But we must realise that this influence is constant and the same for the whole organism.

2. Place a starfish on its back. The arms move and twist about, and the tube-feet are strongly protruded. If a small pebble be laid on one of the arms near the tip, the tube-feet adhere to it and the arm-tip bends round it ; the neighbouring tube-feet are more strongly protruded ; those on other arms are little affected. But if in its varied excursions another arm so turns over as to reach with its tip the rock-surface, the attachment of neighbouring tube-feet spreads, and the tube-feet elsewhere are withdrawn, including those attached to the pebble which may be dropped. And if two arm-tips, say (1) and (3), nearly simultaneously start the righting behaviour, one or other soon relinquishes hold.

3. Young eels, or elvers as they are called in the West country, may be seen in great numbers near the water's edge of estuary streams in the Spring. In the running water they swim persistently up stream. To leave the sea where they have been hatched and to reach sweet-water pools is the plain-tale outcome of this behaviour. Place some of the little fellows in a bowl and stir so as to set the water in circular movement, most rapid near the periphery. They all swim against the current near the edge of the bowl. Reverse the direction of stirring. Every one of them turns round and forges up stream in the new direction. In an estuary they swing to and fro with the flow and ebb of the tide. But under estuarine conditions there is more prolonged ebb than upward flow. Hence there is an up-stream balance to the good. Under such behaviour many of them are bound to reach their destination.

Later in life, however, after they have grown and

thriven in their freshwater habitat, and when the period of sexual maturity approaches, they swim with equal persistence down stream. Place one in running water ; with the current it goes. That is now the plain-tale behaviour in relation to the stream in its flow. To leave the sweet-water pools where so much or their life has been passed, and to reach the ocean where they spawn, is now the outcome of this their later behaviour. If they just go on and on down stream, many of them, should they escape eel-traps and the like, are bound to get there.

This plain tale may be extended under further observation so as to give the complete life-history from hatching, say in the Sargasso region, as precedent (l), to fertilisation of ova, as consequent (n).

§ 8. *Interpretations of Plain Tale*

The three examples I have adduced in illustration of what I speak of as a plain tale are taken from such behaviour as may be observed in organisms of low estate. The bean, the starfish, and the elver, severally behave in certain given circumstances which we may call the situation, and in each case the acts afford instances of a plan or routine of action such as may be observed in respect of any bean, starfish, or eel, in a like situation. I use the word " plan " or " routine " for that which the observer judges to be common to the several instances, in the same sense as one speaks of the plan of events in the atom or in some chemical transaction. So far, even in plain tale, one takes the given instance with reflective reference to what we judge to be the plan common to all such instances. And so far one interprets.

In the case of the eel I glanced at the whole life-history so far as it is known. One could in like manner take the whole life-history of the bean, or of the starfish. But any such life-history can be told in plain tale of that which observably happens. What one then says is : On the basis of plan so far as known through observation of instances, " this " episode has such and such a place in the normal routine.

So far as the plain tale is concerned, the trained observer in his detailed work deals with some phase of current behaviour such as may conveniently be symbolised (as above) by l, m, n. This he selects so as best to focus the inquiry in hand, having due regard to the influence of external events on the organism that thus behaves. And on these terms it is clear that one may, on our principles, substitute willow-wren, water-vole, monkey, or man, for bean-plant, starfish, and eel. Only for convenience of treatment—since we must begin somewhere— did we start with instances of behaviour which may be observed in organisms fairly low down in what we commonly call the scale of life.

In some respects it would be more convenient to start with the behaviour of man and work downward to the bean than to start at so low a level as that at which the plant stands, with a view to working upwards to human conduct. But our theme is emergent evolution ; and our hypothesis is that from first to last two stories of the onward advance in events may be told. Where there are stories to tell it seems better to go forwards from the beginning than backwards from the closing chapter to the introduction. None the less if we seek to participate in writing the interpretative stories, if we wish to review them in retrospect, if we feel that passages here and there, nay, perhaps whole sections, need continual revision in the light of further and fuller evidence, we must consider the end of the stories, up to date, in the upward course of events.

We are committed to a two-story hypothesis because, on review of the evidence, this, as I think, best enables us to interpret the facts that are given in all plain tales. What for us does this imply? Taken in conjunction with unrestricted concomitance, it implies (1) that any selected episode in any given plain tale is susceptible of a two-fold interpretation (*a*) in terms appropriate to physiology, and (*b*) in terms appropriate to psychology; (2) that under (*a*) the story deals with action under influence, with reaction in response of the organism as a whole, and with such action and reaction as occurs in the train of intervenient events between stimulation and behaviour, while under (*b*) the story deals with accompanying enjoyment and with mental reference correlative with influence under (*a*); and (3) that, though each story throws light on the other, neither story as such *makes* the other story what it is. Taken in conjunction with emergent evolution there are further implications to be considered later on.

It should now be clear in what sense I differentiate a plain tale from a story. By a story of this or that plain-tale episode I mean one which *interprets* either for that which deals analytically with part-action, that is, for the branch of science that " teaches concerning the functions of the special organs " (p. 19). But is this what most people, who in some measure accept it, understand by " behaviourist psychology " ? (*cf.* § 27).

I am concerned chiefly so to clear the ground as to render comprehensible my own hypothesis, namely, that not only in human affairs, but in all cases of behaviour, there is a two-fold story—the one a life-story, the other a mind-story. It is avowedly naturalistic. But, if the radical behaviourist says : Never, even in human affairs, is there more than one story ; or if the animist says : Never, in the whole range of life and mind, is there only one realm of events ; then their hypotheses differ from mine.

The three hypotheses may be thus summarised :

1. *Radical behaviourism*—one story only, substantially physiological and biological.

2. *Naturalism*—a two-fold story of physiological and mental events in concomitance.

3. *Animism*—two different stories of interacting events in disparate realms of being.

With regard, then, to the plain-tale behaviour of the elver forging up stream (1) it may be interpreted in terms of radical behaviourism. Here there is denial of any enjoyment or any mental reference on the part of the organism. (2) It may be interpreted in terms of two-story naturalism. Here there is attributed to the eel current enjoyment and at least non-cognitive reference, probably not a little cognitive reference in detail correlative with influence received. (3) It may be interpreted in terms of animism. Here, in the disparate realm of being to which the anima belongs, there is retention of the past in " memory," there is an end in view to be attained however dim and vague may be the envisagement of that end, and there is endeavour to reach that end under an " urge " that drives onward to its goal.

All three hypotheses should be treated with respect since they are widely held with conviction in all sincerity. Each is still on trial. If I advocate one of them in the two-story hypothesis, I may at least ask for a patient hearing.

§ 9. *Guidance, Trial, and Error*

The bean, the starfish, and the eel exhibit a sequence of *acts*, or instances of whole-action behaviour, in plan or routine which is disclosed to the reflective observer. The net result of such a series of acts is its *outcome*. One may say, then, that in accordance with routine the behaviour has *direction* towards its outcome.

May we say that there is *guidance* towards that outcome as an end in view? On the animistic hypothesis, that in effect is what we should say. The direction of behaviour is always expressive of guidance by the anima ; and the urge of behaviour onwards towards its outcome is always due to " hormic " activity. Nay more, it is said that only on this understanding may we properly speak of an " act " ; for an act betokens an agent, and in our present context the agent is the anima that possesses the organism.

before I actually saw him in the lime-tree; there is the initial *non-cognitive reference* that accompanied the cochlear pattern in the internal ear before matters went any further. This, in our adult life, is so masked by higher level reference that it is presupposed rather than disclosed by analysis. It is the starting-point of all reference.

Let us concentrate attention on the mid-level of cognitive reference. My leaning forward and turning my gaze to the tree-top, with expectation of seeing the thrush as I had seen him before, affords an instance of guidance in act. Such direction of behaviour with an accompanying mental factor of guidance comes into the field of personal experience and of inference coincidently with prospective reference (prevision) and some foretaste in enjoyment. This implies revival; it does not necessarily imply retrospective reference. What seems essential is some mental forewarning in the light of which behaviour may be such as to forestall the coming event.

Such in brief is the nature of guidance in the two-fold story I advocate. I can, at present, only give to it tentative expression. Where some immediately precedent determinant of direction in the one story is accompanied by prospective reference in the other story, there is, in the two-fold story, something emergently new—namely, guidance. The future is not yet ; we can only deal with it in terms of probability based on our knowledge of routine. When there is prospective reference, a new factor is introduced into the formula in terms of which the probability is evaluated.

On this showing, the advent of guidance marks a

critical stage in the ascending evolution of reference. Since this evolution is concomitant with that of physiological processes, every item gained through behaviourist treatment is in place within the life-story. But in so far as the *radical* behaviourist finds no evidence for a mind-story, I part company with him ; and in so far as I, on my part, find no evidence for a disparate realm of mental being, I part company with the animist.

To come back, then, to our bean, starfish, and elver, the question arises : Is there guidance under cognitive reference ? As a matter of opinion, after weighing the evidence to the best of my ability, I hold that there is, even in the elver, no such guidance in respect of the behaviour *regarded as a whole*, though there may be guidance in the details within one link in the chain of episodes. In other words, an interpretation in terms of an enchained series of acts having direction to an outcome, but without cognitive provision of the next link in the chain, is, as I think, adequate and sufficient. That is why I have grouped them together as lower forms of behaviour.

It must, however, be realised that any of these lower forms of behaviour, even in plants, *can be* interpreted in terms of cognitive reference if we credit the being that behaves with prevision of that which is coming in the course of normal routine. And if it be held that there is in the mind of that being a mental plan of the routine, and that he " recognises " that the next step to be taken *in act* shall be such as will accord with the next step *in the anticipatory plan in mind*, the whole procedure can there are or may be mental accompaniments of the several physiological states. But, speaking of the reactions, he says : " If they are preceded or accompanied by a common physiological state, this will serve formally as an explanation of the common reaction fully as well as would a common state of consciousness."

It seems open to us, then, to interpret trial and error *of this kind* as affording no evidence of guidance with prospective reference.

§ 10. *Trial and Error under Canon of Emergent Interpretation*

At the emergent level of mind where reference is not only cognitive but is also reflective, there is, in its distinctively human form, an end in view ; there is endeavour to reach it by some means ; there is the quality of enjoyment we call satisfaction when it is attained.

What is this end in view ? In us it is highly complex. In brief it is, so to speak, a binocular or stereoscopic combination or synthesis of two ends —sometimes analytically distinguished as practical and theoretic. The theoretic end is an anticipatory plan in idea or " schema " which shall enable us to interpret events. The practical end is guidance in executive action or conduct in some concrete situation. What one wants is a better plan in mind as a guide to action, and better action as contributing to a more adequate plan in mind. Each furthers the advance of the other. Synthetic or " substantial " development of both together is the end in view in that which we commonly speak of as rational procedure.

At this level of reflective reference—which the child may have reached at the age of, say, three years—methodical trial and error with fully conscious intent plays a leading part. Recall Professor Dewey's characterisation of " how we think." A difficulty in some problem or in some practical situation is at first rather vaguely " felt " ; its locus is defined ; a way out of the difficulty is suggested ; this clue is focussed and elaborated in thought ; then it is tested in combined plan in mind and execution in act. There results a Yes or No attitude of, perhaps, provisional acceptance or rejection, with the joy or sadness in success or failure. Reflective trial and error is contributory throughout.

At the mid-level or cognitive stage of the evolution of reference there is what may also, as we have seen, be spoken of as trial and error. In a difficult situation a way out is *found* ; but it is not *sought* with reflective reference in accordance with some such schema as that which Professor Dewey regards as typical in thought. The animal has learned to act in a number of ways which have been endorsed by success—ways which seem to justify the inference that there is in the mind-story prospective reference to, and expectation of, what is coming in the outcome, but has not yet come in this current instance of the normal routine of action. It has come on previous occasions though it has not yet come on this occasion. But this difficult situation is new and more or less off the line of routine. That is why we speak of it as presenting a difficulty. It seems on the outcome, and perhaps also on its utility. The immediate outcome in (1) is detachment of the ring from its frame. In (2) it is the securing of a bit of fish outside the cage. In (3) it is what we regard as escape. From the frankly plain-tale standpoint (difficult no doubt to preserve) it does seem justifiable to speak in each case of trial along four lines of action, error along three, and success only along the yes-line.

But when we pass to interpretation the observable differences in (1), (2), and (3) demand careful consideration. And the question then arises : Is *the interpretation of trial and error* in all cases the same ? The radical behaviourist may say, Yes it is ; and (3) affords the clue. The animist on his part may say, Yes it is ; and (1) affords the clue.

For the former there is no mind-story, so *that* for him is out of count. On our hypothesis plain-tale trial and error may best be interpreted differently at the three levels I have distinguished in the mind-story as I read it. But since that which is observed at the bottom level *can* be interpreted in top-level terms, why should it *not* be thus interpreted ? Some say that it *should* be. What do we mean when we submit that it *should not* ? We mean that this interpretation is not in accordance with our emergent schema. " Should " or " should not " depends on the hypothesis which is accepted as a policy.

Some thirty years ago I accepted as part of my policy in comparative psychology a rule which I may here restate. In no instance should we interpret an act as the outcome of a higher mental process if it can adequately be interpreted as the outcome of a process that stands lower in the psychological scale.

In the light of emergent evolution this policy and the canon which it implies may be extended in range. In no instance should we interpret events in terms of concepts appropriate to a higher level of emergence if they can adequately be interpreted in terms of concepts appropriate to a lower level of emergence.

If this policy be accepted we should not interpret the lower forms of trial and error as affording evidence of trial and error of the kind that characterises reflective procedure.

of life, more and more does the behaviour and organisation of a living entity depend on *what it is*, less and less is current action determined by the circumstances of the current time-being.

And, on our hypothesis, what an organism is, that it is no less in mental regard than in physical and physiological regard. Could we but learn to read it, there is always, under duality of nature, a mind-story of intrinsic enjoyment accompanying every changing phase of physiological poise throughout the persistent being of the organism ; there is also the further mind-story of extrinsic reference, cor-relative with influence received from without.

But in life-regard the highest of known organisms starts on its individual life-history from the fertilised ovum. There is, in plain tale, embryonic and later development on a plan or routine of events. This plain tale is fairly well known. Tentatively at least a physiological story can be told in analytic terms of " stimulus and response." The plain tale, thus supplemented by physiological interpretation, is behaviouristic in the broad sense. We believe, however, that there is a mind-story. At a stage of the individual life-story that we are beginning to descry, reference, thus far non-cognitive as I phrase it, becomes cognitive and prospective—just how we shall have to consider. At a far later stage it passes to the much higher reflective level. That it does so you and I here and now stand as reflective witnesses. *This* story is other than radically be-haviouristic. It tells not only of action under influence, but of purely mental fields of reference.

For us, then, there is, under the given duality of

nature, a two-fold story of the same course of events in development. And at a critical stage of this two-fold story there comes with the advent of prospective reference—and not before—guidance in a sense of this word which seems consonant with inference from observation. But this critical turning-point in the two-fold story occurs quite late in the evolutionary advance of the storied events. On our canon of emergent interpretation, therefore, the guidance it implies should not be accepted at a stage of evolution, or of individual development, prior to the advent of prospective reference.

In this lecture we are concerned with plans of development prior to its advent. We may not introduce cognitive guidance—still less reflective guidance—until interpretation without it seems to us to be inadequate. But quite early in human life—and in many episodes of animal life—such interpretation without it seems to me to be wholly inadequate. That is where I part company with the radical behaviourist. None the less a wide range of instances of whole-action behaviour and a still wider range of life-organisation can, and on our principles should, be interpreted without introducing the concept of guidance.

There is, we think, no more call to invoke guidance in our sense of the word—that which implies prospective reference—where the substantial and determinate plan of organisation in a living plant or animal is the subject-matter of inquiry, than there is where integral entities of far lower emergent status are under consideration.

In any integral entity living or lifeless, what I

speak of as substance and stuff may be distinguished.
Under a different terminology they together constitute the *whole*, while the items of stuff, severally
regarded, are the *parts* within the whole.   On this
understanding the part is what it is only in substantial relation to other parts within the whole ;
and the whole is what it is only in virtue of the
substantial relation of its parts.   Cut out any
integral part, or even render it different, and the
integral whole is no longer the same entity that
it was, though more or less substantial likeness
may persist.   This is profoundly true of the living
entity.   In the organism whole and parts change
hand in hand so long as life persists—that is, so
long as this example of substantial plan persists.
This is worthy of all the repeated emphasis it receives.   But I contend that it is simply untrue to
the facts to say that this is a criterion that serves
in principle to distinguish living organisms from all
lower integral entities.   It is every whit as true in
principle of the atom, of the molecule, of the
crystal unit.   That, too, in each case, is not only the
additive sum of its parts.   In that, too, whole and
parts co-operate to constitute one natural cluster of
events.   In that, too, as I put it, there is substantial
unity indivisible and pervasive of the entity.   One is
not denying the greater complexity and multiplicity of items of stuff or the enhanced richness of
substance in the organism.   That, for us, would be
to deny its specific emergent status.   I do venture
to deny the time-honoured assertion that we have
here something that distinguishes the living entity
in a sense utterly different from the something that

distinguishes the crystal unit from the molecule. It probably arose through the tendency to compare organisms *as integral entities* with *merely resultant aggregates* in the inorganic realm.

If, in the inorganic realm, we deal with integral entities, there seem to be, according to Sir William Bragg (Brit. Assoc., Toronto, 1924),

"three types of assemblages of matter. The simplest is that of the single atom, as in helium in the gaseous state, in which the behaviour of every atom is on the whole the same as the behaviour of any other. The next is that of the molecule, the smallest portion of a liquid or gas which has all the properties of the whole ; and, lastly, the crystal unit, the smallest portion of a crystal (really the simplest form of a solid substance) which has all the properties of the crystal. There are atoms of silicon and of oxygen ; there is a molecule of silicon dioxide, and a crystal unit of quartz containing three molecules of silicon dioxide. The separate atoms of silicon and oxygen are not silicon dioxide ; in the same way the molecule of silicon dioxide is not quartz. The crystal unit, consisting of three molecules arranged in a particular way, is quartz."

Here we have an ascending hierarchy. On the first level, proton and electrons as items of stuff go together on a determinate plan in substantial unity. On the second level, the items of stuff are the atoms evolved at the first level. They go together on a new determinate plan, one in substance. On the third level, the items of stuff are the molecules

evolved at the second level. They go together (are
" arranged in a particular way ") in a still richer
mode of substantial unity. Furthermore, in each
case the new entity has new intrinsic qualities, and
new extrinsic properties in relation to other entities.

Such is the nature of emergent evolution in the
inorganic realm. It is a far cry to the living entity
which stands on a specialised line of evolutionary
advance. Here certain primitive events of what
we call the physiological order—the bioses—are the
new items of stuff. Do they go together on a new
and distinctive plan, substantial and determinate ?
Does this plan fall within the comprehensive plan of
emergent evolution ?

§ 12. *Mechanism and Monadism*

May one say that recent inquiry within the realm
of inorganic events has thrown much light on their
mechanism ? This is often said. What does it
mean ? I find it difficult to say. I think it may
mean something quite different in accordance with
the context in which it is used. But there must be
something in common to the use of the same word
in more than one context.

Clerk Maxwell, when a boy, was wont to ask of
everything : " What's the go o' that ? " Nor was
he content with a vague reply, but would reiterate,
" But what's the *particular* go of it ? " There is,
I think, a sense in which answers to what we picturesquely call nature's questions in terms of " particular go " may be regarded as answers in terms of
" the mechanism." When we learn in detail the

steps subordinate to the reaching of some observed outcome, we have so far gained knowledge of the natural mechanism. It may be some factor which has hitherto been overlooked.

There is, for example, an older and a newer interpretation of the process of " sedimentation " in an estuary. Particles ranging from coarse sand to fine silt fall at different rates. In the older interpretation, put crudely, the rate of fall could be calculated if the weight and the size of the particles were given. But the facts of observation were found not quite to accord with calculation based on such purely resultant treatment. Professor Joly has now shown that we must reckon with " ionisation " as a factor. May we say that the mechanism of sedimentation is thereby better understood ? If so, have we anything more in principle than a better, fuller, and more detailed interpretation of the course of events on some determinate plan, itself better known ? When we say, as often enough we have to say, that this or that course of events is such and such, but that the exact mechanism is not at present known, do we not mean that the whole determinate plan of these events has not yet been discovered ?

There seems to be a determinate plan of the uranium atom, of its dissociation, perhaps of its evolutionary history. In each case we may ask : What is the mechanism ? In each case the answer is given in so far as the whole sequence of intervenient events between this phase and that can be set forth in due order. I take it that if it be shown that a molecular stage always intervenes between that of atomic constitution and that of the evolution of the crystal unit, Sir William Bragg indicates an important feature in the mechanism of crystal production. But the heart of the matter is determinate plan.

If now we pass from the not-living to the living, and if we regard the course of events in the living entity as affording instances of some determinate plan, the intervening steps within that plan are conveniently earmarked as the mechanism in terms of which the observed outcome may be interpreted. From the evolutionary point of view we search for as simple an illustration as we can find.

Take, then, this condensed statement of Dr E. J. Allen's summary of Dr Wager's observations on Euglena.

"In a very crowded culture the organisms aggregate into clusters beneath the surface-film. The flagella then cease to work, and the cluster sinks to the bottom. Thus the individuals are spread out by the action of the downward current, and when they are sufficiently wide apart, the flagella again begin to move, carrying the organisms in a more diffuse stream to the surface. If the conditions be kept uniform, a circulation of Euglenas, falling to the bottom by gravity when the flagella are stopped, and returning to the surface under flagellate action, will continue for days."

Now we may speak of flagellate action as the mechanism for return to the surface. But this action alternately stops and starts again. What is the mechanism here? In plain tale it is correlated with crowding and scattering. To account for